V-22 OSPREY

An
AEROGUIDE SPECIAL
by
ANTHONY THORNBOROUGH

Breaking with TRADITION

The postwar world witnessed the advent of ever faster, higher-flying aircraft as the droning of propellers gave way to the whine and supersonic bang of turbojets. Advances in related aerospace materials similarly raced ahead as aluminium and titanium-nickel alloys were tamed, opening up manufacturing possibilities into the realms of light, swept structures possessing immense strength. As these new sleek designs thundered aloft into the stratosphere, life for the hard-pressed Army and Marines on the ground seemed to trudge on as it had for the years, eclipsed by the glamour of the high-performance Air Force hardware. However, a revolutionary process was under way: the flimsy looking helicopter, employed initially as a scout and casualty evacuation craft in the late stages of World War II and the Korean conflict, quietly prospered. By the early 1960s this largely unsung hero of the lower skies had grown and been adapted to numerous roles, helping to usher in the new American 'airmobile' concept which was first put to the test in the long and traumatic war in Vietnam. In the steamy, exacting jungles, squads of helicopters ferried the troops to battle, evacuated their wounded, and replenished the 'grunts' with fuel, food and ammunition, as the combined rotary-winged war machine was refined to something akin to a scheduled hit-and-run taxi service! To the Marines, the swirl of the sabre was reborn in the chop of the mechanised rotor, while the Army's cavalry could once more blow its horn!

The success of the helicopter during America's struggle in South-East Asia, and the many other briefer conflicts which had similarly taken British and French forces to such hot-spots as Malaysia and North Africa, underlined the need for an even better support machine: one which combined the advantageous vertical take off and landing (VTOL) attributes of the rotary wing with the ruggedness, speed and endurance of fixed-wing aircraft, principally to bypass the need for paradrops which are always so costly in men and *matériel*. The lessons did not go unheeded, yet they have taken decades to mature into practical solutions. Over the past thirty-five years, hundreds of tons of metal and millions of man-hours have been invested in the design and fabrication of a plethora of demonstrators aimed at exploiting this alternative technology. The most successful of these hybrids have fallen into several distinct categories: compound autogyros, tilt-ducts, tilt-rotors and tilt-wings, all of which are capable of lifting off like a helicopter and then 'converting' to more speedy, horizontal flight, with top speeds well

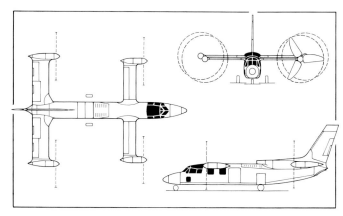

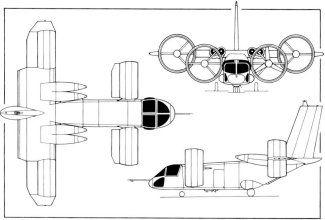

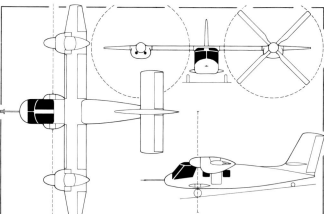

The world's first tilt-wing aircraft was the Boeing Vertol 76, known to its developers the US Army and the Office of Naval Research as the VZ-2. Its entire wing assembly pivoted to provide VTOL flight.

With tufts stitched to its newly skinned latticework, the radical VZ-2 made its maiden flight on 15 July 1958.

Early VTOLS and convertibles. One of Britain's contributions to postwar VTOL development was the Fairey Rotodyne (far left, top), a potential forty-passenger hybrid which made its first transition to level flight in April 1958. It was cancelled four years later (*Westland*). Curtiss-Wright's X-19 convertiplane, also known as the X-200 (left, top) took to the air in November 1963, powered by a pair of Avco Lycoming T55-L-5 turboshafts which drove four airscrews. The prototype was lost before full transition to horizontal flight could be accomplished. The Bell X-22 tilt-duct (far left, bottom) was evaluated by a tri-service team from March 1966 and flew some 50 sorties annually before being handed over to Cornell. The wing-mounted fans were driven by four General Electric YT58-GE-8D jet engines. The compact Westland WE-01 tilt-rotor concept (left, bottom) was known to its designers as a 'VTOL convertible' and relied on four engines for flight safety. It would have been able to carry five passengers or 1800lb of cargo.

beyond the régime of the theoretical 200-knot limitations of the rotary-wing (which, incidentally, has only recently been challenged by Westland's radical BERP-bladed EH-101 and the more revolutionary, but so far only paper, X-wing helicopters).

The noisy compound autogyros of the late 1950s and early 1960s, notably the unique jet-tipped British Fairey Rotodyne and rather different, contra-rotating Soviet Kamov Ka-22 'Hoop', were machines beckoning for, not answering, a market need and consequently never gained much favour (political procrastination, prevalent on both sides of the Iron Curtain, was of no further help); while the heavy jet-powered tilt-ducted machines, the Doak Model 16-cum-VZ-4 and Bell X-22A among them, did not fare well in terms of payload, despite the exciting nature of these exploratory designs. By far the best prospects lay with the two remaining contenders, the tilt-wings and tilt-rotors, which appeared to meet all the performance criteria.

The tilt-wing is the simpler, more pragmatic of the two: a variable-incidence, hydraulically operated pivot-wing housing engine drive, propellers and the kitchen sink, is jacked up for take-off and landing and simply clamped shut for horizontal flight. At first, the concept seemed ridiculously simple – and it worked! The first of the breed to take to the air was the Boeing Vertol Model 76, known to its co-sponsors the US Office of Naval Research (now Naval Air Systems Command, or NAVAIR) and the US Army as the VZ-2. It was an odd-looking but sporty little two-seater. Built by Boeing following a 1956 contract award, it comprised a cockpit bubble poached from a Bell Model 47 married to a metal latticework, T-tail and 26ft-span tilt-wing. An 860hp Lycoming YT53-L-1 turboshaft was bolted to the delicate fuselage and drove the two tailed-mounted fans, plus the all-essential pair of paddle-bladed airscrews interconnected via a cross-shaft. It made its initial, tentative vertical flight on 13 April 1957 and the first of 34 successful complete transitions on 15 July the following year. The featherweight Model 76, which grossed in at a mere 3,200lb, took off and landed much like a clumsy helicopter, employing its rear-fuselage ducted fan for yaw, T-tail fan for nosing up and down and differential airscrew pitch for roll; as the wing took over the lift function, routine ailerons, elevators and rudders were phased into play. In 1959, with contractor trials over, it was handed to NASA-Langley in Virginia where it eventually amassed over 450 flights before its retirement to the Smithsonian in Washington DC six years later.

Follow-on full-scale tilt-wings, including the big Hiller X-18, five LTV-Hiller-Ryan XC-142 prototypes and trio of Canadair CL-84 Dynaverts, represented a major departure. Helicopter cyclic, collective and pedal controls were replaced by conventional aircraft stick, rudder pedals and throttle plus new tilt-wing switches, so that the types more closely resembled traditional fixed-wing aircraft. All three models received a thorough and promising work-out over land, desert and sea but, alas, never quite made it into the order books. A series of fatal crashes (some attributed to mechanical failure, others to pilot error) gradually signed their death warrants. The biggest obstacles confronted were inefficiency in hover when compared to the major rival, the tilt-rotors, and hazardous lateral instability – particularly in strong crosswinds, or in gusty updraughts generated by airscrew downwash – which was apt to dip the wings into the ground. Noise and discomfort in the cabin also made them unpopular with many of their test pilots, despite the fact that these capacious machines, grossing up to 20 tons, were allegedly much easier to fly than the helicopter, and dramatically faster too. All tilt-wing programmes had foundered by 1974, though advances in stability augmentation, propulsion and materials in the intervening two decades, which offer the much sought-after trim and power-to-weight ratio, may give rise to a partial resurrection of the concept during the 1990s.

Far more promising were the tilt-rotors, which introduced a fixed aerofoil supporting a pair of pivoted contra-rotating rotors to achieve transition from vertical to horizontal flight. The tilt-rotors represent a far more natural progression from the helicopter, yet far outclass it in terms of speed and endurance. To their credit, these demonstrators have enjoyed sustained development ever since the first example, the piston-powered Transcendental Model 1-G, commenced its ground tests in 1951. The 1-G took to the skies on 6 July 1954 and made its first complete transition five months later. Tragically, it plunged into the River Delaware the following year after 20 hours' flight time had been logged, but all was not lost: Transcendental's co-founder Bob Lichten, who had been instrumental in designing the company's follow-on Model 2, liaised with and soon afterwards moved to Bell Helicopters in Arlington, Texas, where he was to head a team which produced the far superior XV-3.

Bell's XV-3 housed its pilot* in a well-glazed cockpit which tapered aft into an empennage sharing more in common with a conventional aircraft. Its cockpit looked fairly traditional too, containing stick and rudder yet incorporating new items more familiar to the helicopter such as a collective pitch lever with integral twist-grip throttle. Rotor tilt was effected by a switch on the control column, with separate switches linked to an epicyclic gearbox to alter blade pitch and engine gear ratio; less strenuous horizontal flight requires less torque, permitting a commensurate reduction in engine rpm with spin-offs such as lower vibration and fuel consumption. It was wise of Bell to take advantage of this, and it has been embodied in all subsequent tilt-rotors. Powered by a fuselage-housed 450hp Pratt & Whitney R-985 radial piston engine which drove a pair of triple-bladed, 23ft-diameter rotors mounted on long masts at the tips of its 31ft-span wings, the first example (serial 4147) was unveiled to the US Army on 8 February 1955 and took to the air six months later on 23 August. However, aircraft 4147 was severely damaged in a hard landing on 25 October 1956, by which time only partial conversion, to 15° tilt, had been achieved. Nevertheless, the foundations of the programme had been securely laid. No 4148 followed on its heels and was subjected to a rigorous pre-flight programme involving wind-tunnel trials with NASA-Ames and static test rig operations with the contractor, during which time the pilots perfected the conversion process in comparative safety and luxury. Systems were also fine-tuned: the electrically driven rotor masts were retrofitted with twin semi-rigid blades which overcame much of the flutter experienced with the original, fully articulated design, while the wing underwent aerodynamic refinements, including the fitting of bracing struts for added strength. The flight test programme kicked off on 12 December 1958 and over the course of the ensuing week the rotor masts were gradually 'stepped down' by the electric motors – 30° by the 17th, 70° by the morning of the 18th, and full horizontal conversion through 90° later that day. Speeds of 120 knots were achieved the following spring as the machine was pushed into a non-stop series of sorties under the auspices of the USAF at Edwards and NASA-Ames in California. By 1966 the XV-3 had accrued 110 full conversions, paving the way for newer and even better tilt-rotors. Only two hurdles remained: performance in horizontal flight, and a reduction in weight to increase the machine's VTOL characteristics. With help from NASA, the solutions were already in the bag.

Three-hundred-knot speeds were envisaged with the follow-on craft, rendered possible by a newly perfected rotor blade which incorporated a varied 'twist' to satisfy both the fine pitch requirements of vertical flight and the coarser, bigger inboard pitch for high-speed horizontal cruise. Airframe aerodynamics and materials made similar advances. Out of the melting pot emerged the ambitious Bell D226 project, soon superseded by the less expensive Model 301 proposal. Excited by the technology and the affordable price tag, contracts were awarded on 13 April 1973 by NASA-Ames and the US Army, who referred to the slinky new 42ft-long design as the XV-15.

Bell's first XV-15, NASA-Ames registration N702NA, was rolled out at Arlington to a tumultuous welcome on 22 October 1976. It exuded modernism. Skids had given way to a retractable tricycle undercarriage and piston engines to a pair of Avco Lycoming LTC1K-4K, 1,550shp turboshafts driving triple-bladed, 25ft-diameter stainless steel rotor blades linked to one another by a mid-wing cross-shaft and gearbox to permit single-engine operations. In its glossy white decor it looked beautiful, and it made its first cautionary hover on 3 May 1977 before being shipped to NASA-Ames for extensive wind tunnel tests. XV-15 No 2, N703NA, began its ground tests at Arlington later that August and made its inaugural hover on 23 April 1979. Seated snugly in the cockpit in their Rockwell LW-3B ejection seats with limbs clamped

---

*There was provision for two pilots in tandem, but weight restrictions meant that only one could be carried.

Boeing tilted wings, but Bell tilted the transmission of its XV-3 (top) to achieve conversion to conventional flight, a feat ably accomplished by the second test-bed on 18 December 1958.

Canadair Ltd's CL-84 tilt-wing demonstrator, and follow-on pair of CL-84-1 Dynaverts which were evaluated by a tripartite US/Canadian/British team at Patuxent River, Maryland, very nearly went into production (above). Only the nosegear still flies, fitted to the XV-15. *Canadair*

Building on their experience with the XV-3, Bell developed the magnificent XV-15 tilt-rotor (right) which made its first full in-flight conversion on 24 July 1979. The NASA-backed effort continues into the 1990s. The pair of XV-15s represented the real precursors to JVX, the V-22 Osprey.

to the cyclic, collective ('power') and pedal controls, on 24 July test pilots Ron Erhart and Dorman Cannon took to the skies to execute the type's first successful conversion, for which the crew received the accolade of the Frederick L. Feinberg Award. The test pilots' job was to confirm that as the machine converted to fully-fledged forward flight the controls would automatically reassume the role of manipulating the wing flaperons, elevators and rudders via the mixing boxes, with a minimum of fuss. In fact, the XV-15s flew like a dream, bringing considerable kudos to Bell Helicopter and opening many doors for ever more high-performance designs, including special-mission, remotely piloted tilt-rotors. Among the many 'firsts' compiled during the XV-15 programme, which was extended well into 1988, were the hoped-for dramatic gains in performance: on 17 June 1980, the type set an unofficial world speed record for rotorcraft when 703 somewhat casually attained 301 knots at 16,000ft; building on the earlier work of the Canadair CL-84 tilt-wing trials on board the USS *Guam*, in August 1982 the XV-15 became the first tilt-rotor to operate from a fully combat-capable Marine assault ship, the USS *Tripoli*; demonstration tours around the United States brought home the message of the tilt-rotor's civil potential; altitudes of 26,000ft were reached; and new rotors were designed, leading eventually to graphite-Nomex fibreglass blades sufficiently rigid and hard-wearing to permit top speeds in the 322-knot régime. The epoch of the tilt-rotor had finally arrived in earnest as the XV-15s logged more than 1,800 conversions. Above all, the programme generated grins of satisfaction in the Pentagon: here, at long last, was their long-awaited VTOL airlifter! In December 1981 the Department of Defense put out a request for proposals for a Joint Services Advanced Lift Aircraft (JVX).

Synthesising their near-forty years of experience, it was inevitable that Bell and Boeing would combine their talents to satisfy JVX and produce the ultimate tilt-rotor. The Bell-Boeing Team was officially formed in April 1982 and went on to submit its preliminary design proposal, based on a scaled-up XV-15, the following February. Within two months a Stage 1 award was received to continue the studies, and by 28 April 1986 this had crystalized into a full $1.81 billion fixed-price-plus incentive contract from NAVAIR to proceed with full-scale development (FSD). As approved, FSD embraces the construction and flight testing of six flying test-beds, along with three partly built, non-flying ground and static test articles (GTAs and STAs) as back-up development tie-down, static and fatigue examples. Navy Secretary of the day John F Lehman Jr hand-picked Marine Colonel (now Brigadier-General) Harry Blot as programme overseer, and formal contracts were signed on 2 May. Additional signatures, bringing the total FSD funding up to two and half billion dollars, were obtained shortly afterwards as numerous Government Furnished Equipment (GFE) suppliers were committed to the project. JVX ceased to be an acronym at this juncture and was christened with suitable ceremony – V-22 Osprey, after the marine bird of prey which can both swoop and hover.

The Tilt-Rotor
REVOLUTION

On 19 March 1989 a historic milestone was reached: at approximately 10.56am, Bell test pilot Dorman Cannon and Boeing tester Dick Balzer pushed on the 'thrust' lever and V-22 No 1, Bureau of Aeronautics number (BuNo) 163911, gently lifted itself from Arlington's Texas airport facility. As planned, the Osprey remained in the helicopter mode for the entire 15-minute hop, performing a variety of mild hover turns. The aircraft proceeded to carry out out-of-ground-effect accelerations and decelerations, with height limited to 30ft. On its third brief excursion from terra firma the Osprey accelerated to a gentle 20 knots before completing the day's outing with a second run-on landing. As the happy test crew posed for publicity photos, Bell President L M 'Jack' Horner proudly announced that 'The Osprey's first flight marks the beginning of an extensive, well laid out flight test effort'. He added that 'There is still a lot of hard work to be done'.

In toto, the FSD involves a full seven-year, 4,145-flight-test-hour programme, 70 per cent of which will be flown by Bell-Boeing Team pilots from their test aerodromes in Delaware and Texas. No 2 joined the test force at Bell in early August, followed by the first camouflaged ship, No 4, at Philadelphia that December. The performance envelope has gradually opened up. On 6 September the V-22's tilt-rotors were stepped down to 45° and on the 14th of the month, at an altitude of 6,000ft, BuNo 163911 successfully completed the first conversion to full wing-borne flight; Bell test crew Dorman Cannon and Roy Hopkins were at the controls during the 155-knot manoeuvre. More recently, on 23 October 1989, the V-22 was pushed up to 250 knots equivalent airspeed, paving the way for the projected service performance of 275 knots cruise, 300 knots dash and 26,000ft altitude as the 'shake-down' tests continue apace.

Inside the cool, all-black cockpit are the principal controls. In common with Osprey's predecessors, these serve a dual role, catering for both pure rotary-winged and horizontal flight. Manipulation of rotor pitch and tilt gives way to flaperons, elevator, rudder and throttle commands as the nacelles swivel down through the 70° mark and Osprey begins to behave like a conventional aircraft. There are several new, albeit subtle features. To facilitate operations at sea, the V-22 places the aircraft skipper in the starboard seat. Typical procedures call for an aircraft to approach the vessel from astern and then alight from left to right; seated in the right-hand side of the cabin, the V-22 commander enjoys an unobstructed view. Oddly enough, the Osprey is the *first aeroplane* to switch to this far more sensible cockpit layout. The initial trio of aircraft have been fitted with Martin-Baker ejection seats, while the follow-on batch, all camouflaged, have cockpits more representative of the production machines. In front of each crewman there is a cyclic stick for pitch and roll, a 'thrust' power lever for lift and forward

A sensational wide-angle view of the first Osprey (right), with tilt-rotors, drooped flaps and trials proboscis at the ready for flight-test work. Stringent ground tests were carried out prior to the first flight to verify the fatigue, design loads and ballistic tolerance of the structure (particularly the critical wing and nacelle assemblies), using a ground test article (GTA) fabricated solely for the purpose.

Bell test pilot Dorman Cannon (right, an XV-15 veteran) and Boeing's Dick Balzer pose for the camera following the V-22's inaugural series of hovers.

Up and away. BuNo 163911 made its first hover on 19 March 1989 (left).

V-22 TEST ASSIGNMENTS

Airframe	BuNo	Primary operator	Evaluation tasks
No 1	163911	Bell	Flight envelope expansion Vibration and aeroelasticity trials Gross weight take-offs and landings High-altitude performance
No 2	163912	Boeing	Primary and automatic flight control system tests Icing trials Handling refinements and demonstration of aircraft flying qualities
No 3	163913	Bell	Flight load tests Vibration and acoustic evaluations Preliminary sea trials Structural capabilities
No 4	163914	Boeing	Climatic tests (static) at Eglin, Florida Prop-rotor performance Initial propulsion studies Field evaluation in USAF Special Operations Forces configuration following full avionics retrofit
No 5	163915	Boeing	Avionics integration Autopilot-coupled flight control Terrain-avoidance/terrain-following radar trials Navy/Marines operational evaluation, with emphasis on US Navy Combat Search & Rescue duties
No 6	163916	Bell	Radiation testing (static) in shielded hangar Demonstration of aircraft equipment Navy/Marines operational evaluation, with emphasis on US Marine Corps transport role

The V-22 lower lobe section (right, top) – the first major subassembly to be completed – on its final assembly jig, with the cabin's protective anti-plough bulkhead jutting out in front.

A peek at the tail (right, centre): the skeletal empennage is seen in the photo at left, the same assembly with its skin at right; the design is conventional but the materials primarily composite. Grumman Aerostructures are fabricating nine of the distinctive twin-tail empennages for the V-22 FSD programme, six for the flying test-beds and an additional trio for static and dynamic fatigue tests. *Grumman*

The dark composite airframe of V-22 No 2 nears final assembly prior to despatch to Bell (right, bottom).

motion (with an integral switch for lateral control) and foot pedals for yaw. Rotor rpm is also a hands-on adjustment. Bell pilot Roy Hopkins reckons 'It will be very easy for both fixed- and rotary-winged pilots to convert to', and that in horizontal flight Osprey behaves much like a big, twin-engined commuter aircraft. This ease of control is crucial, and it must be verified during the latter stages of the FSD when service pilots get to grips with the aircraft. The Marines remember some hard-learnt lessons. Back in the early 1970s the Corps initially put its best pilots in the new AV-8A Harrier, with the inevitable result that the jocks reported it 'a piece of cake to fly'. Caution was subsequently thrown into the wind as the Marines assigned inexperienced, less capable apprentices to the type, which soon afterwards began to log a harrowing accident rate. However, as Bell-Boeing take time to remind everyone, 'V-22 represents the world's first production tilt-rotor built from the ground up to serve the requirements of all four US services'. More than 9,000 hours of wind-tunnel operations, including sub-scale models of the rotor, have gone into stability, and in excess 1,000 hours of ground-based simulations in the full-motion cab preceded the V-22's maiden flight. Human engineering factors have consistently been treated with priority.

Under the FSD, Bell is responsible for fabricating the Osprey's wings, nacelles, transmissions and rotor hub assemblies and integrating the Allison powerplants, while Boeing is taking charge of the aircraft's fuselage, overwing fairings and avionics and splicing the tail empennage. In all, some 1,500 suppliers located in 44 States and overseas are producing components directly under the Bell-Boeing Team. Each of the primary contractors is swapping

The manufacture of composite structures is a highly automated affair. Here (below left) an Ingersoll machine demonstrates the tape-laying process used to build up structures prior to curing.

The first cured wing section, with integral stiffeners, ready for the V-22 (below right). The process bonds the tapes and fibres to produce structures which offer immense strength yet lightness and considerable resistance to corrosion.

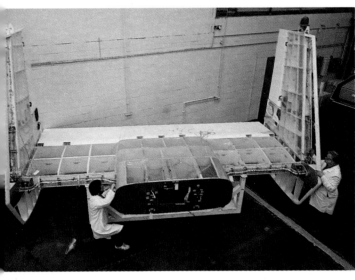

The first forward-swept wing structure was completed in May 1987 (far left, top).

GTA wing and nacelles mounted on Bell's rig for shake tests (far left, centre).

The second set of wing and nacelles on the production line, unbuttoned and displaying part of the transmission (left). The engines are linked by a cross-shaft and mid-wing gearbox to ensure safe flight in the event one engine fails.

The polished lines of V-22 No 2 as it nears completion (left, bottom). The noticeable kink in the tail is designed to provide greater clearance for the 6ft-high cargo hold. The black pin stripes are anti-skid walkways. *Grumman*

Fully mated, FSD V-22 No 2 undergoes shake-test preparations with its electrical flight control systems receiving special scrutiny (below). Systems reliability is another big 'plus' of the Osprey, incorporated from the outset.

parts by air, permitting final assembly of the prototypes to be carried out in both Arlington, between Dallas and Fort Worth, and in downtown Philadelphia, Pennsylvania, ready for initial development and qualification flight-test operations. Production machines will similarly roll out from both plants.

At first glance, the V-22's computer-aided structural design looks conservative. However, the materials represent the leading edge of technology. In contrast to its all-metal forebears, more than 70 per cent of Osprey's 12,500lb structure is fabricated from composites, carefully laid and cured and then spliced together like a giant model kit. The forward-swept wing is made chiefly from Hercules IM-6 graphite/epoxy solid laminate, applied unidirectionally to give optimum stiffness while the fuselage and Grumman-built empennage and twin tail incorporate additional AS4 graphite fibre materials. Many airframe components, such as stiffeners, stringers and caps are co-cured with the skin panels, providing 'cleaner' subassemblies possessing fewer fasteners or potential fatigue trouble-spots. The composite airframe was a 'must' in order to achieve the necessary stiffness and lightness for V/STOL (the structure weighs 25 per cent less than a metal counterpart of the same design) and to provide resistance to corrosion in a salt-water operating environment – the plague of aluminium. The end result is a machine capable of lifting three times its own structural weight. Increased resilience to fatigue and ballistic damage are other key properties of the composite airframe. Tests have demonstrated that customary fatigue crack propagation, particularly around troublesome holes, does not occur even after the structure has been cycled to its ultimate load for two life-times; instead, the millions of fibres continue to carry the stress, so that it fails in a 'soft and slow' manner. A mere 1,000lb of metal is being used in the V-22's structure, comprising a modest total of 92,000 fasteners, control surface hinges, and copper mesh laminated into the outer skin to provide protection from lightning strikes.

The overall empty weight has inevitably grown by up to 1,000lb as the FSD progresses, but the 'Tiltrotor Team' aim to hack a ton of flab from the aircraft by V-22 No 16 as the learning curve climbs and improvements in the design are effected (Bell-Boeing are offering expenses-paid vacations to Hawaii as an incentive for practical weight-reducing measures suggested by its engineers and assembly workers!), all geared towards meeting the guaranteed 31,800lb limit. Indeed, when the No 1 airframe was ceremoniously towed out into the open at Arlington on 23 May 1988, the waiting crowd were impressed with the compactness of Osprey, particularly in the light of its projected payload and performance specifications. For short-haul combat sorties, the V-22 can carry as much as 20,000lb of cargo internally. Total JP5 fuel capacity in the maximum configuration of thirteen tanks – three in the sponsons and the remainder in the wing – provides 2,015 US gallons, excluding the optional cabin fuel tanks, which all adds up to an impressive amount of 'go-juice'. Internal space is similarly more than adequate. Currently occupied by test calibration equipment, the 57ft 4in-long fuselage contains

V-22 MAJOR CONTRACTORS

Bell Helicopter Textron Inc	Wing, nacelles, transmission and engine integration; major assembly
Boeing Helicopters	Fuselage, empennage and overwing fairings; integration of digital avionics
Allison Gas Turbine Division (General Motors)	T406-AD-400 turboshaft engines

V-22 SUBCONTRACTORS AND GFE SUPPLIERS

Aeroquip Corp	Hydraulic and fuel system hose lines and related components
Allied Signal	Swashplate actuators; full-colour multi-function displays
Aydin Vector	Distributed data acquisition (checking) systems
Control Data Corp	AN/AYK-14 mission computer
Dowty Aerospace	Main landing gear, rudder and ramp actuators
GE Aerospace	Digital fly-by-wire flight control system
Grumman Aerostructures	Aft empennage and tail
Hartwell Corp	Access panel latches
Hercules Aerospace Co	Airframe graphite/epoxy composite materials
Huck Manufacturing Co	Fasteners
Hughes Aircraft Co	AN/AAQ-16 Infrared Detection Set (IDS)
IBM Federal Systems Div	Tactical sensor and avionics integration
JET	Standby Attitude Indicator
LTV Aircraft Products Gp	Landing gear drop tests
Litton Poly-Scientific	Wing-fold wire-twist capsule
Litton Clifton Precision	On-board oxygen/nitrogen (OBOGS/OBIGGS) concentrating systems
Lucas Aerospace	Pylon, wing-stow and wing-lock actuators; full authority digital engine control (FADECS) and back-up analogue systems; nacelle ice protection
Moog Aircraft Controls Div	Flaperon and elevator activators
Parker Bertea	Hydraulic and pneumatic actuators and fuel systems, including wheels and brakes
Pratt & Whitney	Second source for turboshaft engines
Speco Corp	Mid-wing gearbox
Sunstrand Aerospace	Prop-rotor and tilt-axis gearboxes; auxiliary power unit (APU)
Systron-Donner Corp	Fire protection systems
Texas Instruments	AN/APQ-174 terrain avoidance/terrain-following radar

The Osprey's unique wing-stow feature (right) was designed to facilitate operations from the crowded flight decks of *Tarawa* class Marine assault ships and the afterdecks of Navy frigates and destroyers. The entire folding process takes 90 seconds and is fully automated.

The Osprey's wing-stow capability is facilitated by a 91in-diameter, fuselage-mounted, stainless steel ring called the 'carousel' (right).

Ready access to the Allison T406-AD-400 turboshaft engines (far right) is provided by a multitude of quick-release panels, some of which serve as steps for rubber-soled maintenance crews.

a 6ft-high, unobstructed 858 cu ft capacity cargo hold which can be fitted with seats or litters and which incorporates rollers to accommodate slide-on/slide-off pallets (which may be low-altitude parachute-extracted, if necessary, out of the rear cargo door).

Another 'first' for Osprey is its built-in stowage features, designed to facilitate operations above and below deck where space is always at a premium. It is a deck spotter's delight. The wing is attached by means of four lugs and slide shoes which turn on a 2½in-high, 91in-diameter, fuselage-mounted stainless steel ring known as the 'carousel', permitting the whole assembly to be rotated parallel to the fuselage. The wing-stow procedure is fully automatic and

Materials used in the primary structure of the V-22 (below left). Breakdown by weight is about 42 per cent composite, 41 per cent metals, 8 per cent fibreglass and 9 per cent other materials. The drawing alongside illustrates the basic Bell/Boeing work-share.

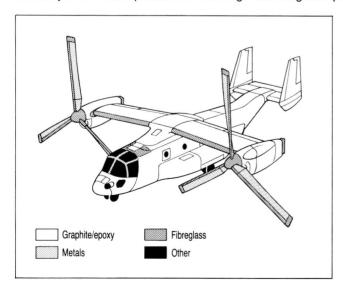

Graphite/epoxy Fibreglass
Metals Other

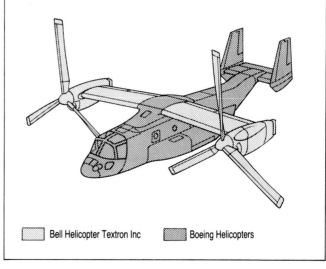

Bell Helicopter Textron Inc Boeing Helicopters

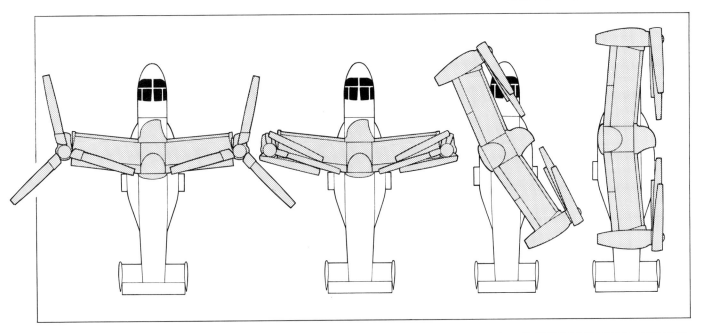

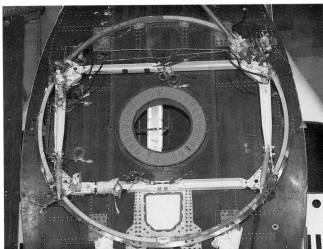

begins with the V-22 in the helicopter mode: the rotors are braked so that the 'master' blades are aligned with the wing leading edges; the remaining blades then flip back alongside the 'master'; the nacelles are tilted to the horizontal; and the entire wing is then swivelled like a turntable through 90°, pushed by a Lucas ball-screw actuator. The integrity of the 1,900-plus electrical connections which pass through the pivot point is maintained by a Litton Poly-Scientific 'wire twist capsule'. The whole process takes only 90 seconds and can be accomplished in gusts of up to 45mph!

Power for the Osprey is derived from its pair of Allison Gas Turbine Division T406-AD-400

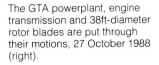

The GTA powerplant, engine transmission and 38ft-diameter rotor blades are put through their motions, 27 October 1988 (right).

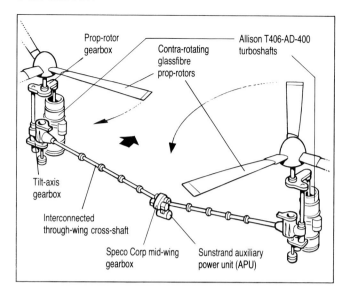

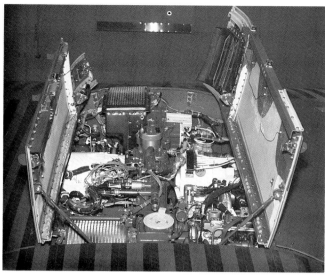

turboshaft engines, sea-level flat-rated at 6,150shp in ambient temperatures of up to 108°F. The powerplant was selected in December 1985 after an intense competition involving Allison, Pratt & Whitney and General Electric, shortly followed by a $76.4 million contract for FSD and qualification testing. P&W were selected by Allison as a qualified second-source supplier three months later. Derived from the veteran T56 turboprop which pushes the venerable Lockheed C-130 Hercules and P-3 Orion (in which it has accumulated a staggering 130 million hours!), the turboshaft adaptation differs from its predecessor by incorporating an advanced full-authority digital electronic control system (FADECS). FADECS is much more sensitive and accurate than the traditional hydraulic-mechanical metering of fuel: it permits the engines to be run close to their operating limit and facilitates automatic engine start, the matching of torque between the two engines and ultimately, greater fuel efficiency. In essence, FADECS reduces crew workload to a simple, single power lever operation, in the sure knowledge that all is being watched and trimmed automatically. The engines also feature an engine monitoring system (EMS) which rapidly diagnoses and isolates patent and emerging faults, helping to pre-empt any subsequent critical failure. The engines' 39 field replaceable units can be serviced by as few as ten tools. Furthermore, the Tiltrotor Team claim that no daily inspections of engines or transmission are required (only a 35-flight-hour/15-day inspection cycle), while as few as 5.5 maintenance man-hours per flight-hour are all that are required to keep Osprey on the wing.

The T406 is a 'free turbine', meaning that the engines can be started while the prop-rotors

V-22 SPECIFICATIONS

Engines: Two T406-AD-400 turboshafts (Engine Spec No 937, fourth draft, 22 July 1985) each rated at 6150shp (4586kW) at maximum and intermediate settings.

Transmission: Take-off rating (sea level, standard day, USMC) 4200shp (3132kW), (sea level, standard day, USN/USAF) 4570shp (3408kW); rating with one engine inoperative 5920shp (4415kW).

Rotor system: Three graphite/fibreglass blades per hub, with automatic powered folding. Diameter 38ft 0in (11.58m); total disc area 2268 sq ft (210.7m²); total blade area 261ft 6¼in (24.3m²); tip speed (cruise) 661.9fs (201.75ms).

External dimensions: Overall length 57ft 4in (17.48m); stowed length 62ft 7in (19.08m); width (prop-rotors turning) 84ft 7in (25.78m); empennage width (aircraft stowed) 18ft 5in (5.61m); overall height 21ft 9in (6.63m); stowed height 18ft 1in (5.51m); blade–ground clearance (helicopter configuration) 20ft 10in (6.35m); static wheelbase 21ft 10in (6.65m); static track 15in 2½in (4.64m).

Internal dimensions: Maximum length 24ft 2in (7.37m); maximum width 5ft 11in (1.80m); maximum height 6ft 0in (1.83m); cabin area 165.09 sq ft (15.34m²); usable volume 858 cu ft (24.30m³).

Weights: Structural design (maximum gross) 30,500lb (13,835kg); empty 31,818lb (14,433kg); operating 32,623lb (14,798kg); design 39,500lb (17,917kg); combat 42,712lb (19,374kg); maximum take-off (vertical) 47,500lb (21,546kg), (short) 55,000lb (24,948kg), (rolling) 60,500lb (27,443kg). Cargo hook capacity (single sling) 10,000lb (4536kg), (dual sling) 15,000lb (6804kg); rescue hoist capacity 600lb (272.2kg). Maximum aircraft hoisting 39,500lb (17,917kg); maximum aircraft jacking 42,800lb (19,420kg).

Fuel capacity: Sponsons 1,228 US gal (4649l); wing (total) 787 US gal (1890l); cabin (self-deploy) 2436 US gal (9221l).

Range: Maximum fuel (self-deploy) 2100nm (3892km); combat (SAR) 1020nm (1890km); amphibious assault 515nm (954km).

Performance:* Maximum speed (sea level) 300kts (556kph); vertical climb rate (sea level) 1090ft/min (330m/min); maximum climb rate (sea level) 2320ft/min (705m/min); service ceiling (both engines) 26,000ft (7925m), (one engine) 11,300ft (3450m); hover out of ground effect 14,200ft (4330ft).

*USMC amphibious assault mission, standard day

The main features of the V-22's transmission system (far left). Access to the mid-wing gearbox and APU is by means of doors on the upper surfaces of the wing centre-section (left).

remain stationary – an important safety consideration on a crowded deck. The power turbine output shaft is also designed to run 'supercritically' with film-damped dynamics, which simplifies lubrication when the engine is running in the vertical position. Emergency lubrication provided by wicks ensures that the shafts can run for over 30 minutes at cruise power. To back up the engines, a 350shp Sunstrand auxiliary power unit (APU) located in the wing centre-section supplies all the necessary electrical and hydraulic power for self-sufficiency at austere locations. The wing centre-section is also home for the V-22's crucial mid-wing gearbox and segmented cross-shafted engine transmission, enabling either powerplant to drive both rotors – another obvious safety measure which, like so many other features, was built upon the technology of the XV-15.

With all working to order, the V-22 can operate at one of three gross weights. In the pure helicopter mode this is limited to 47,500lb. However, a pilot can begin Osprey's transition to fixed-wing flight on the runway by tilting the prop-rotors forward 20°, effecting a wing-assisted, short-running take-off in about 500ft, to haul 55,000lb aloft. For ferry or self-deployment missions, when the cargo hold is equipped with auxiliary fuel tanks, a rolling take-off at the maximum gross take-off weight of 60,500lb is permissible. STOL as well as VTOL operations will be routine from shore bases.

Many of these diverse technologies are already proven in rotary- and fixed-wing aircraft, but what makes the Osprey so impressive is that it represents the first wholesale application of them all in one aerodynamic package.

A proud moment for the Bell-Boeing Team as FSD V-22 No 1 (BuNo 163911) is unveiled to a 2,000-strong crowd on 23 May 1988 (below).

The first Osprey displays its temporary, water-soluble, USMC livery (approximating to FS595a 34095 field green and 35237 grey) which it wore for a short while for the official roll-out (above left). Operational MV-22s will wear a similar but longer-lasting version of this battledress, introduced by FSD ship No 4 which flew for the first time on 21 December 1989.

Wing dihedral, sponsons and wheel track are evident (above) as the podgy V-22 poses for the cameraman.

Like its predecessor the XV-15, the Osprey is a true tilt-rotor design (left), carried aloft by its six graphite-fibreglass rotor blades which incorporate a specially engineered twist to provide optimum vertical and horizontal pushing power. In the STOL take-off mode they help with the burden of a thirty-ton load.

Following the ceremonial roll-out, V-22 No 1 was withdrawn back under wraps where it switched to a white decor trimmed with red (top right); Nos 2 & 3 wear similar schemes. Three months of ground tests preceded the maiden hop, with the first run-ups commencing on 28 December 1988.

The V-22 tipped its nacelles down 45° on a 6 September 1989 sortie (above right) and on the 14th completed the first successful conversion to full wing-borne flight, at 6,000ft (right). At the helm were Bell test pilots Dorman Cannon and Roy Hopkins, who had practised for the event in the Bell CT6 visual database simulator.

Integrated TECHNOLOGIES

While Bell race ahead with the pure flight trials, Boeing and subcontractor IBM Federal Systems Division are concentrating their energies on integrating the digital nervous system of the Osprey. Finally defined in March 1988 following three years of rapid development, the avionics suite is one of the most technologically advanced, fully interactive packages to be fitted to any modern aircraft, designed around an 'all-glass' cockpit designated the Navigation, Control and Display (NC&D) subsystem. It is all-solid-state, managed by dual Mil Std 1553B databus systems and IBM's JVX Avionics Support Software (JASS), interlinked with banks of engine, flight control and mission computers to provide an unprecedented degree of automation – safety and reliability being at the forefront of the system architecture.

Considerable feedback was gained from prospective service pilots when the foundations of the cockpit were originally laid down and this has been reflected in the ergonomic, symmetrical layout which is a boon to pilot 'situational awareness'. Dominating the dashboard console are four Allied Signal IP-5555 full-colour Multifunction Display (MFD) TV tubes, each of which can be selected to flash up any one of a number of synthesised graphic presentations: Vertical Situation Display, an attitude director which embodies cyclic and throttle control cues for good measure; the Horizontal Situation Display, resembling a glorified compass, which defines heading and desired track; a projected digital map display, tied to a terrain storage system (which will, in time, be garnished with alphanumeric pointers and command-and-control information down-linked by support aircraft); and sensor imagery. With four MFDs to play with, a whole host of information is sensibly condensed and presented to the crew in easy-to-digest format, providing navigation solutions and defining course, altitude and airspeed reference paths (based on the pre-take-off flight-plan), which can then be flown manually or automatically. It takes all the guesswork out of flying.

The first two Ospreys on the wing (right), with red-tailed No 2 in the lead slot. The unique right-hand cabin location of the aircraft commander dictates flying formation off the port wing, though the interactive multi-function cockpit displays provide full authority from either seat. The overhead, side and knee windows provide excellent visibility for both crew members, aided by a rear-view mirror.

The V-22 features a comprehensive 'glass' cockpit (left), devoid of traditional gauges and toggle switches. Four large, full-colour MFDs and a pair of smaller CDU TV displays furnish all the flight information, commanded by push-buttons. The responsibility for integrating these displays and the remainder of the avionics rests with Boeing and IBM.

These clever features extend to the pair of digital data-processor Control Display Units (CDUs) and the bank of illuminated push-button keyboards, located in the lower centre of the main instrument panel. There are no isolated or awkward-to-reach, antiquated toggle switches to fumble for; instead, by keying the appropriate commands, data may be accessed on the status of aircraft subsystems or certain operations initiated – be they automatic start of the APU, engine or wing-stow sequence, fuel balancing, tuning the communications navigation and approach aids such as the full complement of UHF/VHF/HF secure voice radios, tacan/VOR and ILS, or activating the electronic warfare kit. Even the fuel gauge employs a liquid crystal as opposed to a 'needles and dials' read-out, the sole concession to traditional instruments being the JET electrical standby attitude director 'ball', wired in purely as a back-up device and to furnish precise read-outs during loiter manoeuvres.

Osprey No 4, BuNo 163914, made its maiden flight on 21 December 1989 from Boeing's snowy test facility in Delaware (right).

Osprey CLOSE-UP

V-22 No 4 under close scrutiny from Boeing Helicopters' resident photographer in January 1990, revealing the aircraft's built-in maintenance features, Dowty-Canada landing gear, cargo door details and other items of particular interest to the modelmaker; the colour scheme is shown in its entirety on pages 28–29. In size and performance the Osprey is comparable to the Grumman C-2 Greyhound.

The digital systems also include the all-important General Electric fly-by-wire Primary Flight Control System (PFCS), triple-redundant like so many of the other subsystems for added safety and reliability. Instead of relying on bell cranks, pulleys, push-rods and cables, the Osprey's hydraulic-actuated control surfaces and rotor swashplates are computer-linked to the cockpit via a myriad tiny wires. This arrangement not only saves weight but also prevents excursions beyond the flight envelope – that is, the computers provide optimum commands to the actuators, completely overriding the crew's inputs in some circumstances to avoid potentially dangerous manoeuvres. In this manner, PFCS can be set to manage automatically airspeed, nacelle tilt, angle of attack and so on to prevent a stall, or to prevent the machine exceeding its design load factors. PFCS is also coupled to the engine's FADECS, and to the triple-redundant (of course) Automatic Flight Control System or autopilot, which is on hand to provide pilot relief, even full 'hands off' flight. PFCS does all the hard work, yet it introduces a modicum of stick and pedal force feedback lest the pilots imagine that they are not in complete charge of flight operations! It all adds up to an impressive package. Gone are the days when separate fuel tanks had to be monitored and manually sequenced to maintain centre of gravity and a smooth flow of kerosene to the powerplants; engine trim is automatic; flight control is fully adjusted by the computers; and the 'all-glass' cockpit provides everything required within easy view of both crewmen. V-22 No 5 is about to embark on the preliminary fully-integrated avionics 'smoke tests' with Boeing at its Wilmington, Delaware-based flight test facility.

Birds of prey are noted for their sharp vision, and the Tiltrotor Team have not ignored this

Further angles (above and below) on FSD No 4's maiden flight, demonstrating the aircraft's slotted 'flaperons' in action and the rear cargo door. Conventional landing gear could be supplemented with skis for operations in cold climates: Antarctic survey teams have expressed a strong interest in a civil derivative.

A multitude of displays is available on the MFDs, as this picture (right) reveals. Among the options are vertical and horizontal flight situation, projected map and subsystem status.

The Hughes infra-red detection set juts out from under the Osprey's nose (above) to furnish high-resolution imagery to the crew, despite darkness, smoke, haze and limited adverse weather. It is a completely 'hands off' sensor which responds to the pilot's head movements, projecting a FLIR image on to the visor. *Hughes*

vital aspect of their new product which lives up to its namesake. Under-the-weather and night-time nap-of-the-earth operations are to be rendered safe by a pair of specially tailored electronic 'eyes' which jut out from the V-22's beak – a derivative of the AN/AAQ-16 Hughes Night Vision System known as the Infrared Detection Set (IDS), and a Texas Instruments AN/APQ-174 multi-mode terrain radar, backed up by a radar altimeter.

Hughes' all-seeing sensor has been in production since April 1985 and applied to numerous combat helicopters (notably the Kaman SH-2F Seasprite LAMPS Mk 1, Sikorsky MH-60G Pavehawk and Boeing CH-47E Chinook) where it is already proving its worth with the US Army and Customs Service. It represents the first completely 'hands off' forward-looking infra-red system to be deployed operationally, servo-linked to respond to air-crew head movements and to project, in turn, a narrow, 6× field-of-view (FOV), TV-quality image of the outside world on to the pilot's visor, permitting heads-up flying in a blacked-out environment. Image contrast and brightness generated by the variable heat sensor are automatically adjusted to the ideal viewing level, while the pilot may call for flight director symbology to be superimposed over the visor imagery further to reduce the need to duck back down periodically to the console. A semi-automatic back-up mode is available for general navigation: with the IDS set at a wide, 1× FOV and its image screened on one of the MFDs, the 'idle' crew member can take hold of a six-inch tracking handle to slew the FLIR about manually, to check on waypoints or to acquire the designated landing zone, or ship, prior to let-down.

Texas Instruments' radar is another piece of proven technology built upon years of

Low-level and night ingress to the drop or pick-up co-ordinates is to be rendered routine by the Hughes Infrared Detection Set, servo-linked to the crew's helmets, though the pilot in this artist's depiction (right) appears to be sporting night vision goggles – a cheaper alternative which may be adopted by the Marines.

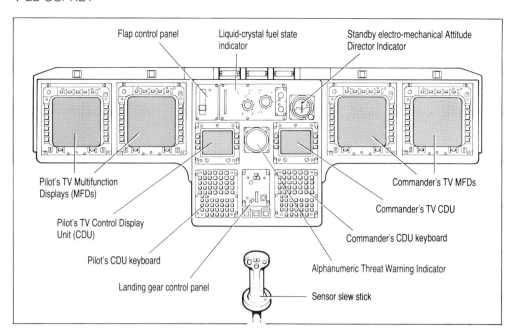

Flap control panel

Liquid-crystal fuel state indicator

Standby electro-mechanical Attitude Director Indicator

Pilot's TV Multifunction Displays (MFDs)

Pilot's TV Control Display Unit (CDU)

Pilot's CDU keyboard

Landing gear control panel

Commander's TV MFDs

Commander's TV CDU

Commander's CDU keyboard

Alphanumeric Threat Warning Indicator

Sensor slew stick

The main features of the V-22's forward console (left). Pilots with an ability to type are doubtless at an advantage!

experience, in this instance with terrain-following systems. Derived from the LANTIRN low-altitude navigation pod (now equipping USAF F-15E dual-role fighters), the scanner generates forward-looking terrain data which are duly processed and conveyed to the autopilot, to permit 'hands off', earth-hugging operations down to 100ft above ground level. In action, the pilot will monitor the FLIR imagery in his visor, fused with radar-derived pull-up cues, and use the information either to hand-fly the Osprey or simply to monitor the proceedings with the autopilot in full authority and with limbs clamped lightly to the controls as a safety measure.

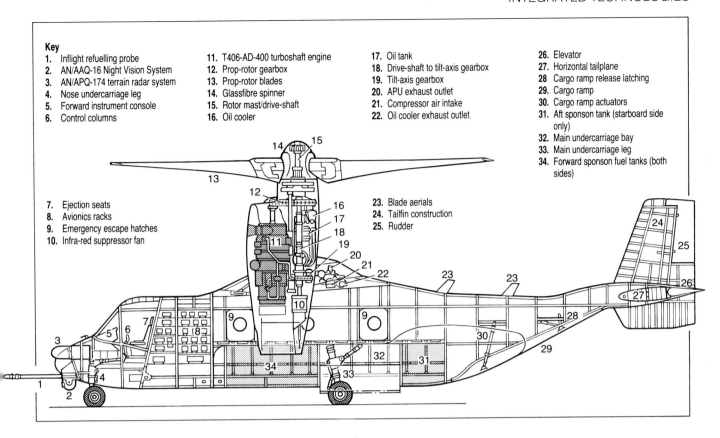

Key

1. Inflight refuelling probe
2. AN/AAQ-16 Night Vision System
3. AN/APQ-174 terrain radar system
4. Nose undercarriage leg
5. Forward instrument console
6. Control columns

7. Ejection seats
8. Avionics racks
9. Emergency escape hatches
10. Infra-red suppressor fan

11. T406-AD-400 turboshaft engine
12. Prop-rotor gearbox
13. Prop-rotor blades
14. Glassfibre spinner
15. Rotor mast/drive-shaft
16. Oil cooler

17. Oil tank
18. Drive-shaft to tilt-axis gearbox
19. Tilt-axis gearbox
20. APU exhaust outlet
21. Compressor air intake
22. Oil cooler exhaust outlet

23. Blade aerials
24. Tailfin construction
25. Rudder

26. Elevator
27. Horizontal tailplane
28. Cargo ramp release latching
29. Cargo ramp
30. Cargo ramp actuators
31. Aft sponson tank (starboard side only)
32. Main undercarriage bay
33. Main undercarriage leg
34. Forward sponson fuel tanks (both sides)

The salient features of the predominantly composite V-22, in its operational troop-transporting configuration (above). The forward cabin door and rescue hoist are located on the starboard side, opposite the avionics rack.

Osprey's cavernous hold (left) can accommodate up to 24 fully armed troops strapped in 'crashworthy' seats, or up to ten tons of cargo. The preliminary FSD machines are fitted with extensive test and calibration equipment.

The first four sets of sensors have been completed at El Segundo, California, and Dallas, Texas, and delivered to IBM for integration work. Full IDS and radar capability is to be incorporated on aircraft Nos 5 and 6 and retrofitted to No 4, all in good time for the operational evaluations which will concentrate on three key mission objectives: BuNo 163914 will act as the USAF Special Operations Forces (SOF) test-bed, BuNo 163915 as a US Navy Combat Search & Rescue (CSAR) vehicle and BuNo 163916 as a US Marines troop cargo ship and equipment 'trash hauler'. All these roles imply assignments that would see the V-22 operating in inclement weather over rugged terrain, on missions that would inevitably involve close contact with the enemy. Built-in protection therefore also features strongly in the Osprey's make-up, to prevent the bird's feathers from becoming unduly ruffled by the opposition.

Additional protruberances planned for Osprey will include a probe for air-to-air refuelling, to enhance the machine's already impressive endurance, together with nose and tail-mounted warning antennae and a self-defence countermeasures kit. Scheduled for full trials on board the pair of Navy/Marines camouflaged test-beds is Honeywell's AN/AAR-47 missile warning set and Lundy AN/ALE-39 chaff/flare/decoy dispensers. The Honeywell detector is designed to pick up ultraviolet emissions emanating from rocket plumes, to provide warning of both radar-directed and otherwise invisible passive-homing infra-red guided anti-aircraft missiles. Threats will be displayed on the mid-dashboard alphanumeric compass rose and relayed to the dispensers to distribute chaff cartridges and flare pyrotechnics at the appropriate moment – either automatically or on crew command via the CDU keyboards. Special equipment envisaged for the USAF SOF configuration includes the Loral AN/ALQ-157 infra-red lamp which generates 'puffs' of distracting energy abeam the aircraft to lure heat-seeking weapons away from their intended prize.

Enemy weapons will also be denied a sure kill by the inherent low-acoustic, infra-red and radar signatures of the Osprey. A suppressor is fitted on the end of each engine nacelle which 'dilutes' and disperses the hot exhaust plume. An anti-plough bulkhead forward of the cockpit affords a fair amount of protection to the crew, while the ballistic resilience of the composite airframe is well established. Safety measures extend to the Osprey's gizzards. Five Systron Donner fire detector/suppressor units have been strategically located in the V-22's wing, coupled to Halon-filled flasks. The system was put through its paces during tests at the China Lake Naval Weapons Center, California, where 23mm rounds were shot into a fuel-filled test sample. The resulting explosion and fire was extinguished in under 40 milliseconds. The current goal is to make the production V-22 invulnerable to the occasional 30mm hit too. Further suppression comprises the Clifton Precision Instruments' Onboard Inert Gas Generating System (OBIGGS) which replaces spent fuel with nitrogen to purge the tanks of volatile, explosive fumes and combustive air. (A related OBOGS oxygen-generating package, also drawing on outside air, feeds oxygen to the three-man crew of pilots and crew chief.)

Should all else fail and a mortally wounded Osprey be obliged to flutter back to earth, Dowty Canada Ltd's main landing gear is equipped with a two-stage shock absorber to cope with a 24fs crash-landing with no adverse effects on the airframe. The LTV Aircraft Products Group are performing the 'crunch' trials and in March 1988 verified the landing gear's ability to absorb

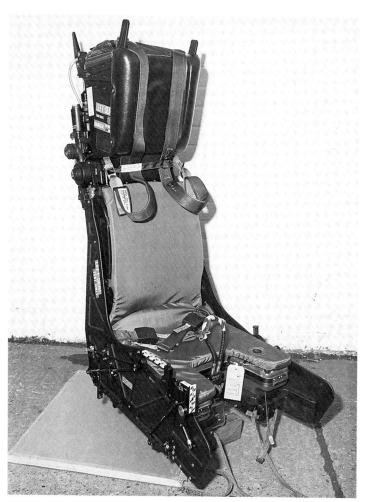

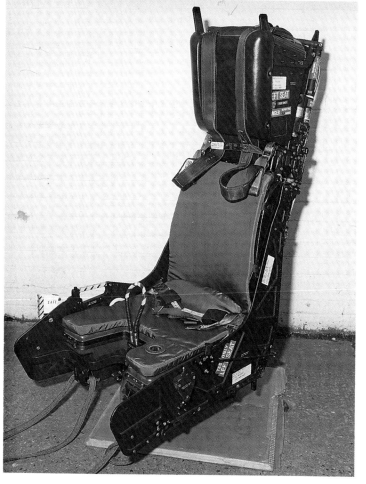

The first trio of Ospreys are each equipped with a pair of Martin-Baker Mk 10 (US10E-1) zero/zero-capable ejection seats (left), complete with left- or right-hand tailored canopy breakers. This test sample is representative of the seats fitted to the actual aircraft. *Martin-Baker Aircraft Co*

Strapped to Martin-Baker's US10E-1 'bang' seat, a suitably adorned mannequin makes a rapid exit from a dummy V-22 forward fuselage (right). Effecting this life-saving emergency egress between the two large, contra-rotating rotors would be a relatively safe procedure, though it is not a prospect test crews relish, for both personal and Corporate reasons! *Martin-Baker Aircraft Co*

most of the punishment during actual drop tests. (The gear is designed to cope with routine 'normal' sink rates of 12fs and 'hard landings' of 14.7fs.) The cross-shafting and mid-wing gearbox come into play in these emergencies to assist a crippled machine in making a safe, relatively gentle recovery in an engine-out situation. Such a procedure calls for a steep approach – an autorotation *in extremis*, should both engines have failed or been knocked out – followed by a short roll on touch-down. Bell test pilot Roy Hopkins claims he has performed single-engine recoveries in the simulator at an all-up weight of 60,000lb (a mere 500lb below the maximum gross STOL take-off weight) and is confident that the real aircraft will perform equally well. 'Crash seats' are to be fitted as standard for all occupants. No wonder Tiltrotor Team spokesman Tom Tripp is on record as having asserted that 'the V-22 is more crashworthy than a helicopter'. He went on to claim that in a 'worst-case' situation, the Osprey's two powerplants and related transmission are designed to break free from the fuselage, thereby avoiding the lethal hazard of the gyrating hardware smashing into the cabin. Based on the impact tests and inherent design features, Lt Gen Charles Pittman, deputy Chief of Staff for Marine Aviation, testified before an attentive Congressional committee that the Osprey is up to ten times more likely to survive a mishap than a comparable helicopter. Maintaining its integrity in this manner, once the dust has settled a crippled, earthbound V-22 may be dismembered, strapped to hoists and airlifted home for the necessary repair job, facilitated by the composite structure which readily lends itself to patch work.

It is this combination of the avionics, self-defence equipment and built-in survivability that makes the Osprey such a rugged machine, ideally suited for a wide variety of military tasks.

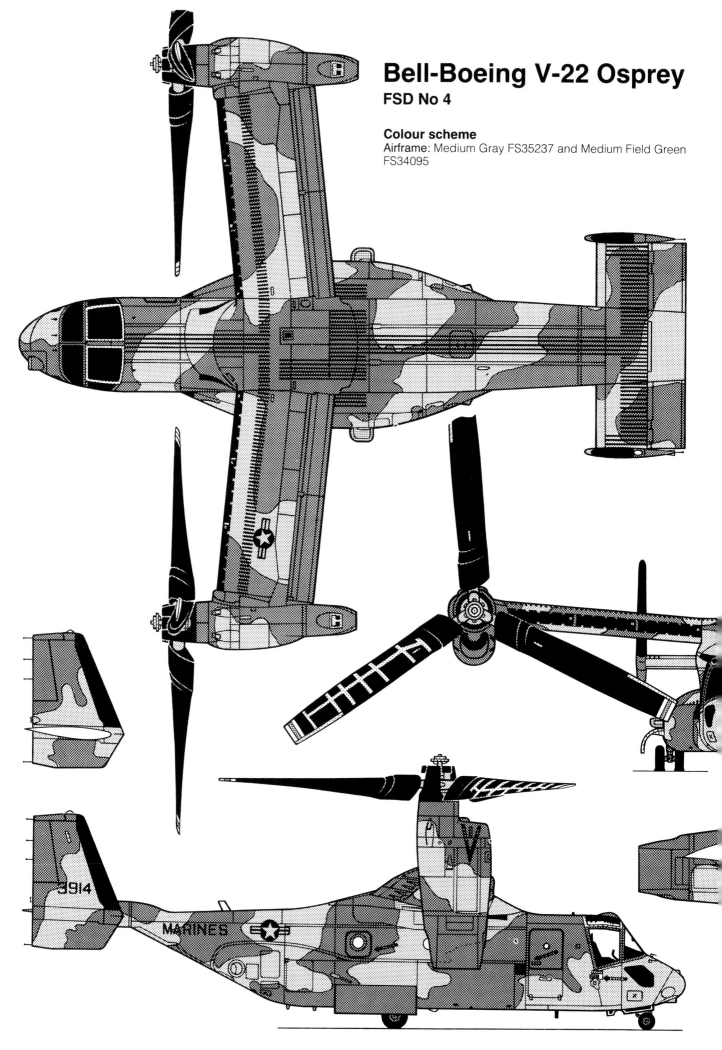

Bell-Boeing V-22 Osprey
FSD No 4

Colour scheme
Airframe: Medium Gray FS35237 and Medium Field Green FS34095

National markings, 'Marines' legends and warning notices:
Black FS37038
Spinners and prop-rotors: Black FS37038
Prop-rotor striping: Yellow
Prop-rotor tips: Red and white
Undercarriage legs: Medium Field Green FS24095
Undercarriage bays: Black FS37038
Leading edges of wings and tailfins: Semi-matt black

1:96 scale

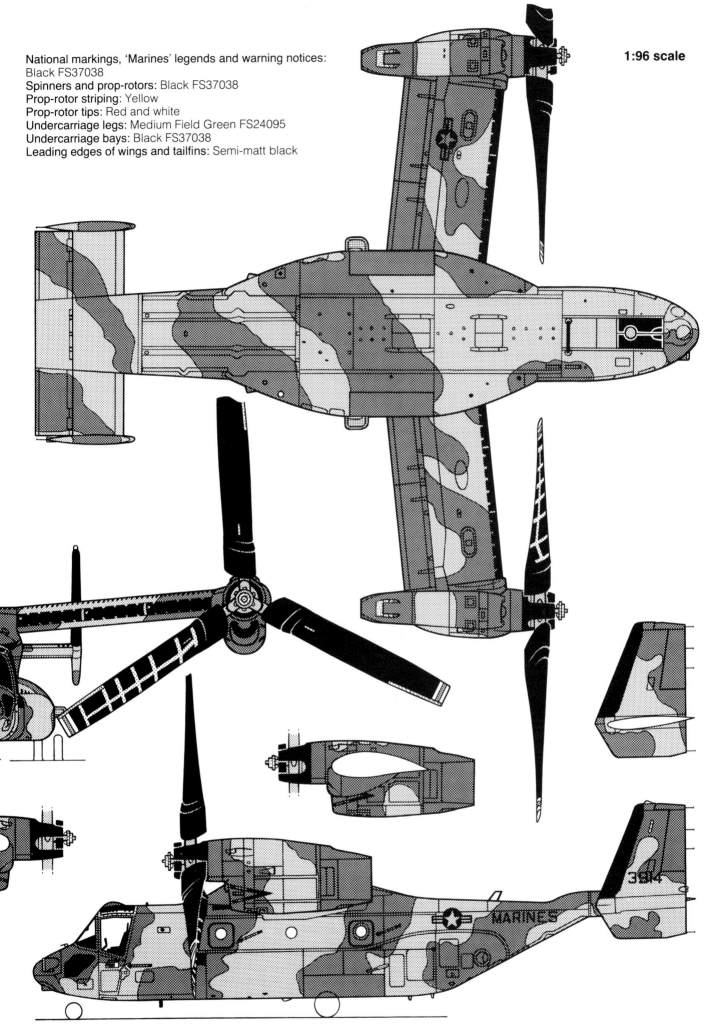

Tilt-Rotor
BIRDS OF PREY

S hould all proceed according to Brig Gen Harry Blot's and the Tiltrotor Team's plans (now a moot point, as will be reviewed later), camouflaged production Ospreys will emerge from the final assembly plants in ever increasing numbers starting in 1992. In all, ten production Lots are envisaged, peaking at 132 machines with Lot 4 in the mid-1990s. Adapted from the baseline FSD airframes to meet the specific needs of the tri-service customers, procurement could eventually total over nine hundred aircraft for the US military alone, comprising four distinct marks.

The biggest prospective operator is the programme leader, the USMC, which is seeking 522 MV-22As – up to 602 if one includes attrition replacements – to support its amphibious assault forces. The Marines have always been enthusiastic about VTOL technology and have taken the plunge: over the past twenty years the cutting edge of their mobile firepower has revolved around the helicopter and potent BAe/McAir AV-8 Harrier, backed-up by longer-legged buzzing F/A-18 Hornets, A-6 Intruder interdictors and radiating EA-6B Prowlers to knock out or neutralise the heavier defences. Osprey, they claim, will enable them to maintain the sharpness of their fighting edge through to the twenty-first century; the heyday of the Corps' well-loved but now obsolescent Boeing CH-46 Sea Knights and still shiny but technologically dated Sikorsky CH-53 Sea Stallions has long since passed.

The key ingredients that make the V-22 so attractive are mobility and endurance. It is not surprising to learn that these factors were at the forefront of the very stringent minimum requirements set down by the Marines for their new JVX combat assault, logistical resupply and aeromedical evacuation (medevac) tilt-rotor: to carry two dozen fully equipped combat troops 200nm and to hover out of ground effect at 3,000ft in 91.5°F temperatures (the so-called 'brick' test) at mid-point; to carry two lots of 5 tons of cargo slung on hooks over a 50-mile radius without a fuel top-up (since expanded to a 15,000lb capability to counter criticism from the Osprey's opponents, enabling the type to haul such loads as the MC4000 fork lift, or HMMWV multi-purpose vehicle, with eight troops internally); to operate from austere bases and amphibious ships in concert with the Harrier, with which it is designed to share certain field diagnostic and repair equipment; and to be capable of self-deployment over a 2,100nm range without aerial refuelling support. Based on the results from the initial flight test programme, all these goals are likely to be exceeded, especially with projected engine and transmission growths from 6,150 to 10,000shp.

The Marines hit an icy, craggy coastline – a scenario which is regularly rehearsed today in Norway using helicopters. MV-22As would swoop in during the initial assault and then conduct medevac and resupply, once the 'grunts' had established a firm foothold.

V-22 MILESTONES

1981	December	Department of Defense (DoD) initiates Joint Services Advanced Lift Aircraft (JVX) project
1982	April	Bell-Boeing Tiltrotor Team formed
	December	Defense Systems Acquisition Review Council (DSARC) Milestone 1 approved
1983	February	Bell-Boeing preliminary design proposal submitted
	April	Bell-Boeing preliminary design Stage 1 award
1984	May	Bell-Boeing preliminary design Stage 2 award
1985	February	Full-Scale Development (FSD) proposal submitted
	June	Bell-Boeing Team begins FSD
	December	Allison selected for powerplant FSD
1986	March	Allison selects Pratt & Whitney as second source for powerplant
	April	DSARC Milestone 2 approved
	May	Bell-Boeing Team signs for full FSD programme with NAVAIR
1988	May	First V-22 prototype rolled out at Arlington, Texas; Dornier GmbH signed up to explore the V-22 market in Germany, following similar agreement with BAe to look at V-22's prospects in UK
	June	Mitsui & Co Ltd and C Itoh & Co Ltd of Japan signed up to explore V-22 market in Japan
	December	First ground run-up tests begin at Bell's Plant in Arlington
1989	March	V-22 No 1 makes first hover at Arlington
	August	V-22 No 2 makes first flight at Arlington
	September	V-22 No 1 tilts nacelles to 45° and later transfers to horizontal flight and 155kts
	October	V-22 No 1 reaches 250kts equivalent airspeed
	December	V-22 No 4 makes first flight at Boeing's Wilmington test facility in Delaware

'Speed is life' – and nowhere more so than in evacuating the critically wounded (left, top). The Osprey is capable of delivering the wounded into capable medical hands in a third less time than it takes its helicopter counterparts at the moment.

The US Navy is considering the acquisition of over 300 SV-22As honed to the anti-submarine warfare mission (left, bottom), operating from carriers, Knox class frigates and Spruance class destroyers to supplement and eventually replace the SH-2F Seasprite and S-3B Viking.

The Army may yet take up its option for 231 MV-22As, which would be deployed in the role of casevac, combat and intratheatre logistics support, as depicted below. The big artillery guns featured in this rendition eat shells at a dramatic rate and require constant replenishment.

According to Bell-Boeing Team studies using Army and Marine Corps statistics as a base for the calculations, the MV-22A could provide double the troop and equipment build-up on beach with 30 per cent fewer aircraft than are required by the current all-helicopter force. Such a scenario would typically call for a combined air and sea assault from LHA Tarawa class vessels, each ship providing up to a battalion of 1800 Marines and their support fire en route to the 'hot landing zone' if equipped with a nose-mounted minigun and mortar and a clutch of laser-guided Rockwell Hellfire anti-armour missiles for use against targets designated by forward-emplaced 'grunts' or Navy SEALs.

The V-22 was conceived as a true multi-mission machine suitable for sea- or land-based operations. The Army's acquisition policy, on their own admission 'presently in complete disarray', may yet take up the option of 231 MV-22A marks for medevac, for long-range combat support, and to meet certain special operations requirements, with such units as Task Force 160 based at Fort Campbell, Kentucky. The Army's short-term need is to be met by 112 specially adapted Boeing MH-47E Chinooks and Sikorsky MH-60K Blackhawks equipped with FLIR and radar, but the performance figures fall short of MV-22 – notably by up to 1,345nm in ferry range and 135 knots in cruise speeds. To the military, there is nothing more frustrating than executing an otherwise successful operation, only to find the 'troops in contact' cut off for want of rapid aerial resupply or evacuation. The Marines are particularly well aware of this need: they have been deployed in over 80 per cent of the near-240 crises that have cropped up since World War II. As one official put it, 'The Marines are an expeditionary force that must be prepared to fight across the spectrum of conflict'. The Marine Air motto proclaims that 'Speed is life!'; only the V-22 Osprey offers that vital lead in performance.

Seafaring salt-water partner the US Navy envisages procuring 50 ghost-grey, five-man HV-22A marks for CSAR and Fleet logistics support, operating up to a 480nm radius to replenish ships in the Vertical-On-Deck role and to pluck downed airmen or SEALs from hostile territory or icy or shark-infested waters, possibly under intense fire. A study put forward by the personable former Navy Secretary John F Lehman Jr also highlighted the need for up to 350 SV-22A models, honed to the anti-submarine warfare mission as replacements for both the SH-2F Seasprite and the ever-growing number of Lockheed S-3B Vikings now adopting an alternative electronic signals intelligence-gathering role. With the capability to zoom over the wave-tops at 275 knots to reach the assigned search zone speedily, then to convert to hover to dip its sensors, the SV-22 may prove to be the ideal sub-hunter. Magnetic anomaly and acoustic detection equipment, backed up by 'smart' torpedoes to dispatch the opposition, would take up the payload, managed by a four-man crew split equally between pilots and a pair of electronic hunters. Osprey measures in at around the size of the Grumman C-2 but is not confined to operations from the giant super-decked flagships like the old Greyhound: VTOL

The floating VTOL war machine (above left): a battalion of Marines and its support armour and artillery, backed up by hovercraft, Harriers and Ospreys, to provide a rapid-response, ship-to-shore strike force from *Tarawa* class amphibious assault ships.

Clean 'em up and green 'em up (above): MV-22As dominate the scene in the assault, demonstrating the tilt-rotor's landing sequence to good effect.

Powerful searchlights illuminate a grateful flyer drifting at sea with only a PRC-90 radio to announce his position (left). Using Hughes' IDS as a search tool, CSAR would be the primary assignment of the Navy's HV-22As. A 600lb-capable rescue hoist is to be fitted as standard equipment. Rotor downwash is very mild directly beneath the aircraft, making pick-ups a relatively trouble-free affair.

Combat SAR is a vital morale-boosting job for which the Osprey is ideally suited. Both the Navy and the Air Force envisage employing the versatile V-22 in this demanding role (right). Osprey's 300-knot dash speed will inevitably save lives.

flight and the self-stowage features readily permit 'spotting' on the cramped aft flight-decks of *Knox*, *Long Beach* and *Spruance* class frigates and destroyers. A Navy tanker derivative is also a realistic proposition: probe-to-drogue contacts with the jet receivers are customarily made in the 250-knot indicated airspeed régime, well within the potential KV-22's performance envelope. With a suitable drum, hose and drogue plumbed into the 16,000lb cargo-hold rigid ferry fuel tanks, regular HV-22As could find a valid niche in the tanking business.

The US Air Force, which figures strongly in the hoped-for multi-service buy, is seeking 55 minigun-equipped CV-22As for its long-range SOF, primarily to augment the latest generation of Lockheed-built, Florida-based MC-130 Combat Talon and AC-130 Spectre Special Operations 'Herky Birds' and to supersede the valiant MH-53J Pave Low 'Super Jolly', currently also tasked with CSAR, as a new V/STOL covert infiltrator/exfiltrator. Ironically, while the projected demand for the CV-22A mark remains at the bottom of the league, this model is gathering considerable support to create one of the biggest buttresses for the Osprey programme in the face of increasing opposition from the Pentagon.

As part of his massive proposed defence cuts, all geared towards addressing America's deficit woes, the cancellation of the V-22 programme was one of the first tasks that newly appointed Defense Secretary Richard B Cheney set himself when he took up office in early 1989. The production Osprey's price-tag has risen slightly, making it an unfortunate target. Cheney's initial attempt with his fiscal chainsaw foundered, but it left plenty of scars. Following a fierce inter-committee altercation in Washington, Congress reinstated Fiscal 1990 funds to the tune of $255 million to continue the six-ship FSD effort, postponing a firm production decision until the following budget review. Then came round two, on 1 December 1989, after Congress had conveniently adjourned for the year. Under the express orders of Deputy Defense Secretary Donald J Atwood, NAVAIR was instructed to cancel $330 million worth of funds appropriated for V-22 long-lead advance production contracts, many already in progress;

this has since been amended to a deferred allocation following a thumb-squeeze from House Armed Services Committee chairman Les Aspin, but is seen as all but ruling out a full production go-ahead. To a great extent, this move has pre-empted Congress's impending critique of the Osprey which was to be based on initial feedback from the FSD, and also upon a Cost & Operational Effectiveness Anaylsis (COEA) due to be published shortly after the up-and-coming Fiscal 1991 budget review in the spring of the new decade.

The COEA study, under compilation for Richard Cheney by the Institute for Defense Anaylsis, focuses on alternatives to the V-22 such as updated marks of the Sikorsky rotary-wings (and the pace-setting Westland EH-101 remains an attractive contender), and is directed at full-scale war scenarios such as a major 'scrap' between NATO and the Warsaw Pact. It may give ammunition to Cheney, and eminent analysts are sounding the warning claxon. Dov S Zakheim, former Deputy Undersecretary of Defense, put his case in the 19 October 1989 edition of the *Washington Post*. To summarise, and echoing the feelings of some twenty-seven Senators led by Osprey-concerned Republicans Arlen Specter and John Heinz, who in a letter to Cheney have urged him to explore the wider applications of the V-22, Zakheim pointed out the fallacy of the COEA: that the Pentagon's favourite hypothetical NATO *versus* WarPac confrontation is a vision of the world which is losing credibility daily. Premier Gorbachev's domestic initiatives (and problems), the Soviet withdrawal from Afghanistan, the emerging Vienna Treaty on conventional forces, the crumbling of the Berlin Wall and a massive knock-on change in political feeling in Eastern Europe all point to new priorities for the US military – that from a pure pre-positioned standing army to a new, flexible defence force able to meet, at short notice, various crisis contingency operations worldwide as a self-deployable, rapid-action task force. This emerging re-patterning of operations has been reiterated many times over the past two decades: the Son Tay prisoner-of-war extraction attempt over North Vietnam in 1970; the *Mayaguez* incident in Cambodia and the pull-out from Saigon, Operation 'Frequent Wind', in 1975; the aborted Operation 'Eagle Claw' in Iran five years later; Operation 'Storm Fury' in Grenada in 1983; and, most recently, Operation 'Just Cause', the December 1989 intervention in Panama. These 'low intensity' actions must figure prominently in any serious appraisal of the V-22's projected roles. In such situations the best available equipment must be on hand: lives cannot be measured solely in terms of cost-effectiveness, and only the speedy, long-legged Osprey offers the all-essential self-deployment capability wrapped up with the necessary agility and survivability features to confront the ever-increasing, insidious threat posed by well-armed terrorists' and despots' anti-aircraft arsenals.

British Aerospace, which is exploring the UK market prospects of the Osprey under a Memorandum of Understanding (MoU) signed with Bell-Boeing in September 1987, have drafted a specification which envisages a tanker model capable of providing up to 13,000lb of 'giveaway' over a 200nm radius (including thirty minutes of loiter time on station) if launched in the running, short-take-off mode; and a very useful 9,000lb of fuel if launched in the pure vertical-take-off mode, assisted by 20 knots of wind-over-deck.

The European and Pacific military markets, being explored under various MoUs with Aeritalia, British Aerospace, Dornier and the Japanese companies C Itoh and Mitsui, remain

A USN Osprey squats on the aft flight deck of a destroyer (above) in its SV-22 sub-hunting configuration. Additional roles include Vertical-On-Deck resupply and aerial refuelling. The contra-rotating blades, aided by a PFCS-assisted gust alleviation mode, provide excellent handling even in windy conditions.

This is the role (above right) in which no other aircraft type can hope to compete: the USAF long-range SOF covert infiltration/exfiltration mission, to extract troops, civilians or captives. Would Operation 'Eagle Claw' have gone differently had Col 'Charlie' Beckwith, Delta Force commander, had CV-22A Ospreys at his disposal? Of the eight ochre-coloured RH-53Ds that took part in the operation on the fateful night of 24 April 1980, only six reached the rendezvous point and a mere one returned to the deck of the USS *Nimitz*.

In scenes reminiscent of Vietnam, troops fan out from the downwash-flattened 'hot' landing zone (right). Latterday missions of this sort could well embrace surprise anti-drug operations – or frenzied, briefcase-laden commuters racing to get to the office on time!

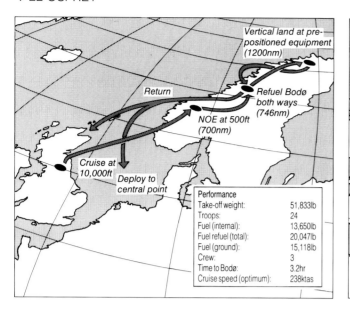

Vertical land at pre-positioned equipment (1200nm)

Return

Refuel Bodø both ways (746nm)

NOE at 500ft (700nm)

Cruise at 10,000ft

Deploy to central point

Performance	
Take-off weight:	51,833lb
Troops:	24
Fuel (internal):	13,650lb
Fuel refuel (total):	20,047lb
Fuel (ground):	15,118lb
Crew:	3
Time to Bodø:	3.2hr
Cruise speed (optimum):	238ktas

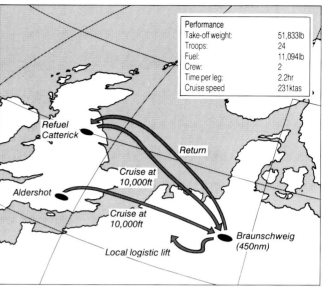

Performance	
Take-off weight:	51,833lb
Troops:	24
Fuel:	11,094lb
Crew:	2
Time per leg:	2.2hr
Cruise speed	231ktas

Refuel Catterick

Return

Cruise at 10,000ft

Aldershot

Cruise at 10,000ft

Braunschweig (450nm)

Local logistic lift

strong potential outlets for additional customised variants of the V-22, which would be backed up by an integrated, allied maintenance network. BAe, for example, have suggested two versions for the Royal Navy, an airborne early warning scout sporting an APS-138 or -145 rotordome, capable of filling a big gap in the UK sea/land defence capability, and an SV-22 derivative which would serve as an anti-ship missileer (when toting Sea Eagle or Harpoon radar-guided weapons), as a mine warfare craft (capable of depositing and clearing the deadly charges), as a CSAR 'picker-upper' and as a sub-hunter (when suitably equipped with sonobuoys and Mk 46 torpedoes). Land-based, Royal Air Force tasks to which the Osprey would also be ideally suited include short-haul transport and resupply, commando assault and rapid reinforcement of Central Europe (a much-needed capability in the light of the Vienna Treaty on conventional forces, which will call for massive reductions in pre-positioned ground forces stationed on the Rhine) – and general SAR, with the V-22 painted in the RAF's favourite rescue livery of Golden Yellow, to pluck 'lemmings' (as the RAF describe seasonal holiday-makers who habitually find themselves stranded on wind-swept rock faces or drifting out to sea!).

The JVX proposal emerged from the exciting XV-15 effort and the lessons learned in many brief 'brush fire' confrontations in South-East Asia, Central America and the Middle East. The US services – and others – want V-22. Equally important, it is imperative that for technological reasons Osprey is not permitted to fade away like its predecessors, relegated to the annals of a once-promising effort that would have helped to maintain America's pre-eminence in aerospace had the production programme not been hacked to pieces in its prime. Its future now rests solely with the people in charge of the purse strings.

Two of the many possible missions for an RAF Osprey, as envisaged by BAe: commando assault on northern Norway (above left) and rapid reinforcement for ground troops in Central Europe (above).

Royal Navy requirements exist for a V-22 AEW platform capable of tracking enemy vessels, acquiring aerial intruders and vectoring Sea Harriers on to enemy 'bogeys' (left). The Westland Sea King AEW which currently fulfils this role is equipped with a much shorter-range Searchwater radar housed in a pivoting, inflatable radome and is severely limited by endurance and weather. *British Aerospace*

Civil TILT-ROTOR

I n their letter to Dick Cheney, Arlen Specter and John Heinz looked beyond even the needs of tomorrow's armed forces to cite 'the extensive commercial applications of the Civil Tiltrotor (CTR)'. The Bell-Boeing Team has been active in promoting a CTR derivative of Osprey, with Sam Mayer and Ron Reber as managers, and have enjoyed the backing of a number of powerful lobbyists. In 1985 FAA Admininstrator Donald Engen sent communiqués to NASA Administrator James Beggs and Secretary of Defense Caspar Weinberger asking for their support for a proposed joint study of the national implications of the Osprey. Engen had been briefed on both the XV-15 and V-22 tilt-rotors by NASA's Ames Research Center and was impressed with CTR potential: oil spill containment (since brought to the fore following the *Exxon Valdez* disaster in Alaska), drug interdiction (a pet project of the former Reagan Administration which President George Bush is anxious to continue), Coast Guard rescue, forest fire control (for example, Yellowstone), air ambulance, priority cargo haulage and, top of them all, the exciting possibilities of city-to-city commuter operations which would bypass the hustle and bustle of, and alleviate the strain on, the major congested airports. NASA-Ames should know: it has been intimately involved with the Bell-Boeing tilt-rotors and tilt-wings for twenty-five years and has on its books a leading exponent of CTR in the form of Dr John Zuk, Chief of the Advanced Plans and Program Office. He points out that a CTR has all the advantages of vertical flight yet can go 'twice as fast and twice as far as the helicopter on one-half the fuel' while offering the comfort levels of short-haul turboprop aircraft. A joint Government study was funded shortly afterwards, sponsored by NASA, the FAA and the DoD, with NASA-Ames taking executive control. In turn, the Boeing Commercial Airplane Company was contracted to perform a market analysis and, in company with the Tiltrotor Team, spent sixteen months exploring the specific opportunities open to a CTR. A series of 'wish lists' were formulated, based on preliminary talks with prospective operators, which led to the draft requirement for a series of craft capable of conveying up to 75 passengers (PAX) over ranges of up to 725nm at cruise speeds of 300 knots. All models resembled the V-22 structurally and technologically, with a view towards, perhaps, parallel production lines. The market place was then re-explored. This identified an international demand for 310 V-22 format CTRs of 31-PAX capacity and no fewer than 1,430 aircraft in the stretched, 39-PAX format by the year 2000 – a mere six or so years following projected CTR certification and the inauguration of scheduled operations!

The initial effort has since swiftly expanded to sixteen separate studies, mostly American Department of Transport, FAA-awarded grants which aim to explore the impact of CTR in a

Bell-Boeing foresee numerous applications for CTR aircraft, both in the form of direct V-22 derivatives and as brand new programmes utilising the manufacturers' hard-earned technology. A selection of possibilities is illustrated below.

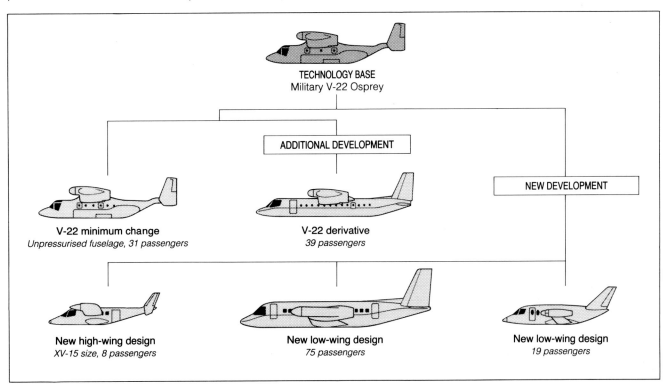

TECHNOLOGY BASE
Military V-22 Osprey

ADDITIONAL DEVELOPMENT

NEW DEVELOPMENT

V-22 minimum change
Unpressurised fuselage, 31 passengers

V-22 derivative
39 passengers

New high-wing design
XV-15 size, 8 passengers

New low-wing design
75 passengers

New low-wing design
19 passengers

given region. The VTOL Intercity Feasibility Study for the Port Authority of New York and New Jersey (PANYNJ), published in June 1987, is just one to emerge. Operating over a 300-mile radius from such downtown sites as the Wall Street heliport in Manhattan, the business community would be free to jaunt north to Boston, west to Pittsburgh or south to Washington DC in less time than it takes to make a comparable journey by jet, the report concludes. Trips of up to 500 miles currently account for over 70 per cent of all domestic flights, and it is all too common to spend more time trundling back and forth to the main hubs – for example, two-hour car journeys through New York to reach Newark, John F Kennedy or Le Guardia, jammed in rows of traffic – than sitting comfortably in the cabin speeding through the air! The PANYNJ study alone has revealed a likely demand for an annual 5–8 million CTR passengers by the turn of the century, capturing up to 60 per cent of the short-haul market. Instrument Flight Rules reliability is seen as crucial in order to weave the VTOL machines into the existing air traffic control network, but Osprey – and all CTR studies are assuming a similar 'glass' cockpit packed with communications and navigation aids – provides this on a plate.

Another major advantage to be reaped is the relatively tiny size and modest cost of the vertiports when compared with the huge acreages of real estate required to accommodate the otherwise inevitable growth of the big strips. Thirteen-plus 4-acre facilities (excluding car parking, which could be placed underground) would be all that is needed to serve the PANYNJ flow. As Mayer has noted: 'For the price of one US $6 billion airport . . . a complete system of vertiports, as well as the aircraft for a commuter system, could be bought and paid for'. Initial studies looking at the transport nets in California, Illinois and Texas are yielding similar conclusions.

Bell-Boeing see the growth of CTR operations arriving in two distinct stages: initially as a 'feed the hub' radial system whereby vertiports serving the big, densely populated conurbations would convey commuters to the major airports for long-haul flights, and out on arrival at their destinations; followed by netted vertiport-to-vertiport 'portal to portal' operations which would bypass the log-jammed hubs. The proposed infrastructure would build on existing heliports as well as newly created vertiports. The major benefits to be reaped in the long term are much reduced congestion (an ailing malady of the clogged-up and growing national transportation systems in North America, Europe and the Pacific Rim, saving time and money to the business world and frustrated commuter and freeing the major airports for the big, long-ranged jets, with spin-offs for the environment), much reduced noise and much reduced pollution.

The price-tag carried by the CTR remains the only contentious issue. $12–16 million for NASA's projected 40-PAX CTR-3900 model is noticeably higher than the price of any of the comparable short-haul, fixed-wing alternatives ($9 million, for example, for the Aérospatiale ATR-42 turboprop). However, cost would inevitably become more favourable if the military Osprey is proceeded with roughly on schedule. There is an important object lesson here. America's roller-coaster success with the Boeing 707 and domination of the civil big-jet market ever since was founded on a massive military order for the very similar KC-135 Stratotanker, which absorbed many of the fixed design, research and development costs to make the début airliner that much more financially attractive to its prospective customers. The military V-22 is another example of leading-edge technology for its day which could usher in a new dawn, this time in commuter travel. The failure to grasp this opportunity will leave a gaping hole in a potentially huge market which may be taken up by overseas competitors: Augusta and Aeritalia of Italy, Aérospatiale of France, CASA of Spain, MBB of West Germany and Westland of Britain are joining forces to settle the preliminary details of their co-operative CTR called the Eurofar, while the Ishida Group of Nagoya, Japan, may bring tilt-wing technology to the fore once again with their TW-68 transport. If America's promising V-22 Osprey effort is squandered, the military tilt-rotor and CTR market will be up for grabs!

The Osprey could be readily manufactured as a 31-PAX or twelve-ton cargo short-hauler. NASA has projected that demand for its stretched, 39-PAX capacity derivative could well approach 1,500 aircraft by the turn of the century.